GOD'S PRESCRIPTION FOR
ENHANCING YOUR LOVE LIFE

LOVE, SEX & LASTING RELATIONSHIPS

CHIPINGRAM

Love, Sex & Lasting Relationships

Scripture quotations marked "NASB" are taken from the New American Standard Bible®, Copyright © 1960, 1962, 1963, 1971, 1972, 1973, 1975, 1977, 1995 by The Lockman Foundation. Used by permission.

Scripture quotations marked "NIV" are taken from HOLY BIBLE, NEW INTERNATIONAL VERSION®. Copyright © 1973, 1978, 1984 by International Bible Society. Used by permission of Zondervan Publishing House.

Scripture quotations marked (TLB) or "The Living Bible" are taken from The Living Bible |computer file| / Kenneth N. Taylor. — electronic ed. — Wheaton: Tyndale House, 1997, c1971 by Tyndale House Publishers, Inc. Used by permission. All rights reserved.

Scripture quotations marked "NRSV" are taken from The Holy Bible: New Revised Standard Version / Division of Christian Education of the National Council of Churches of Christ in the United States of America. — Nashville: Thomas Nelson Publishers, c1989. Used by permission. All rights reserved.

Scripture quotations marked "KJV" are taken from the Holy Bible, King James Version, Cambridge, 1769.

Produced with the assistance of Kaleo Ranch, LLC. Graphic Designer: Joey Wofford. Walk Thru the Bible project staff includes: David Ball, Rebecca Gregory, and Lauren Rife.

Small Group Kit: ISBN 1-885447-43-4
Workbook: ISBN 1-885447-45-0
All rights reserved. *Printed in the United States of America.*

CONTENTS

Love, Sex & Lasting Relationships

Where's the Love?

by Chip Ingram

It seems everybody these days wants love, sex, and a relationship that lasts. It's talked about on TV, portrayed in the movies, and is the most common theme pined in popular music. There's even landmark legislation being introduced in government — all in an effort to allow people to find their own version of a fulfilling happily-ever-after.

But here's the question: if all our resources are focused on the pursuit of true love, great sex, and meaningful relationships, why are we drifting further and further from all three? Research clearly shows that love, family, and yes, even sex, are more elusive than ever. In the wake of the free-love generation, divorce has become an epidemic. As a result, generations of children are struggling to define the missing pieces of the relationships they've been denied and are now unable to cultivate in their own families. Meanwhile, sexual dissatisfaction has become the centerpiece of books, talk shows, and the booming pharmaceutical business. With all that turmoil, fewer and fewer relationships stand a chance of lasting.

At the root of it all is a belief system poisoned by hidden distortions. Without realizing it, we've bought into an approach to love that simply doesn't work.

But it doesn't have to be this way! In *Love, Sex & Lasting Relationships*, we'll uncover God's prescription for experiencing true love, maximum sexual satisfaction, and relationships that last a lifetime. It's an ancient approach that still bears a revolutionary spirit. And if you're willing to re-examine your world, you can be on your way to discovering the love of your life, sex as God intended you to enjoy it, and a relationship more fulfilling than you ever imagined! Let's dig in together!

Keep Pressin' Ahead,

Hollywood's Formula for Lasting, Loving Relationships

INTRODUCTION

Everybody wants love. In fact, our search for love is the number one theme of today's popular movies, music, and literature. And this is nothing new. As documented in ancient Greek literature, the Old Testament, and the writings of William Shakespeare, love has always been a major part of the human experience. It preoccupies our hearts and shapes our life's pursuits. At the deepest level, we were created to connect with another person spiritually, emotionally, and even physically.

So here's the question. If we've been at this so long, how come we're so bad at it? Why are most of those love songs about break-ups, pain, dysfunctional relationships, and unfulfilled dreams? If God created us for love, why is it so difficult to find it?

In this session, we'll examine two methods of looking for love. One leads to bliss and fulfillment, and the other leads to heartbreak and destruction. By the end of this session, you'll be able to recognize which one is most commonly portrayed in our culture today. And you'll understand the flaws that lure us into disappointment. Best of all, you'll learn God's plan for experiencing the love, sex, and the lasting relationship you've been looking for all along.

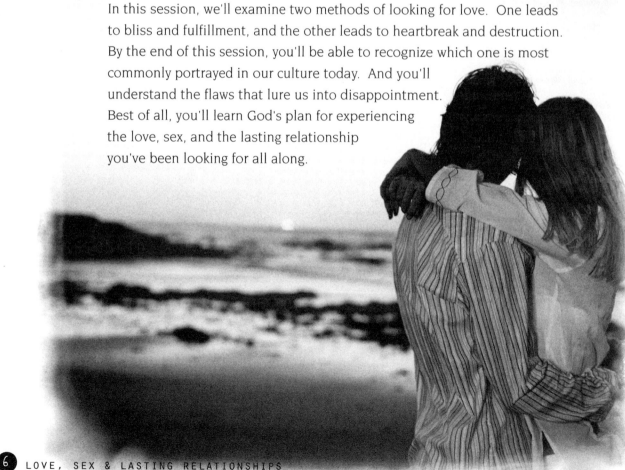

Video Notes

I. HOLLYWOOD'S PRESCRIPTION FOR LASTING RELATIONSHIPS

1. _____ the right person.

2. _____ in love.

3. _____ your hopes and dreams of future fulfillment on that person.

4. If _____ occurs, repeat steps 1, 2, and 3.

II. THE RESULTS

III. GOD'S PRESCRIPTION FOR LASTING RELATIONSHIPS

[1]*Therefore be imitators of God, as beloved children;* [2]*and walk in love, just as Christ also loved you, and gave Himself up for us, an offering and a sacrifice to God as a fragrant aroma.* ~ **Ephesians** 5:1-2 (NASB)

1. _____ the right person.

2. _____ in love.

3. _____ your hope on God and seek to please Him through your relationship.

4. When failure occurs, repeat steps 1, 2, and 3.

IV. THE RESULTS

*"Marriage is not so much about **finding** someone as it is **being** someone."*

~ *Charles Shedd, from* Letters to Karen

Discussion Questions

1. What are some examples of popular movies, music, television, magazines, etc. that sell Hollywood's prescription for lasting relationships?

2. How have the things you watch, read, and listen to shaped what you believe about love and sex? In what ways have you bought into Hollywood's prescription for lasting relationships?

3. In your pursuit of a lasting relationship, have you been more focused on finding someone or on becoming someone? What has been your result?

4. Which is easier: to become an imitator of God or an imitator of a Hollywood role model? Explain.

5. Of all the qualities you look for in a mate, which ones do you think will be the most important to you long term? Do you possess these qualities? If not, what will you do this week in your pursuit to "become the right person"?

Hollywood's Formula for Lasting, Loving Relationships

SESSION 1 KEYS

● Popular culture tells us: "Find the right person and fall in love."

● God tells us: "Become the right person and walk in love."

ACTION STEPS

It's important to look back over your life and consider the different influences that have shaped the way you approach love. Was your idea of "love" impacted by a favorite TV show, a favorite movie, or a group of friends? When you stop and think about it, many of our ideas about life come from some unusual sources. And if we're not careful, we can end up believing things without examining the truth behind them.

In the chart below, list the most influential factors in forming your understanding of love. Then give a brief "statement of belief" to describe what you were taught to believe as a result of your exposure to each influence.

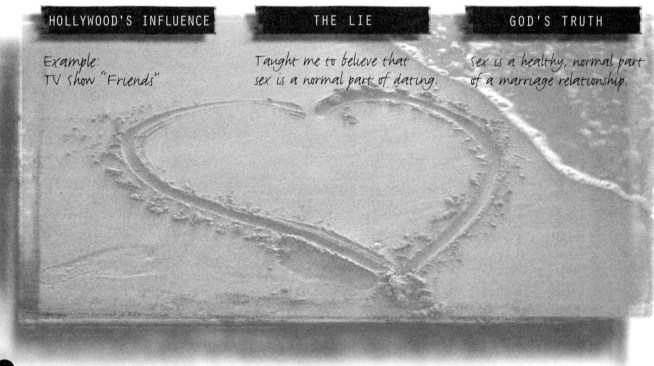

HOLLYWOOD'S INFLUENCE	THE LIE	GOD'S TRUTH
Example: TV show "Friends"	Taught me to believe that sex is a normal part of dating.	Sex is a healthy, normal part of a marriage relationship.

AT HOME

God created love and sex. That makes Him the best source for advice on cultivating a lasting relationship. As we learned in this session, the first step to adopting His approach to love is to become an imitator of God. In the spaces below, list two or three steps you could take this week to become an imitator of God so you are prepared when He brings a mate into your life.

MEMORY VERSE

Therefore be imitators of God, as beloved children; and walk in love, just as Christ also loved you, and gave Himself up for us, an offering and a sacrifice to God as a fragrant aroma.
~ Ephesians 5:1-2 (NASB)

Two Models for Lasting Relationships

INTRODUCTION

Our distorted understanding of love is one of the greatest plagues in our culture today. We don't know how to *be* in love because, in part, we don't understand how to *fall* in love. What should it look like to start down the path to a lasting relationship? On one hand, Hollywood tells us how to do it. But God's method is entirely different. So when it comes to having a picture of what it means to fall in love, even most Christians don't have a clue. As a result we drift along, following our feelings and hoping for the best.

But God doesn't want our future hopes of marriage to be subjected to such uncertainty. Just as He created love, sex, and lasting relationships, God also created a set of principles that can guide us with confidence as we cultivate these important areas of our lives.

In this session, we'll see how Hollywood has actually taken God's process for falling in love and turned it upside-down. We'll explore the five levels of intimacy in a love relationship, and the order in which God intended for us to take them. And when we're finished, you'll be able to determine what you need to do next in order to begin looking for love in all the right places.

Video Notes

HOLLYWOOD'S FORMULA

spiritual

social

psychological

emotional

physical

GOD'S PRESCRIPTION

physical

emotional

psychological

social

spiritual

1. Ask: Is this person a committed _____?

2. Observe the person _____.

3. Get to _____ each other.

4. Keep your emotions behind _____ lead.

5. Come together _____.

PERSONAL EVALUATION & ANALYSIS

Which triangle most represents your approach to building lasting relationships?

Which model would you like your present and/or future relationships to look like?

What specific steps do you need to take to begin implementing God's secret to a lasting relationship?

"True love comes quietly, without banners or
flashing lights. If you hear bells,
get your ears checked."
~Erich Segal

Discussion Questions

1. How successful has your current approach been in developing and sustaining long-term, healthy relationships that include all areas of intimacy — the spiritual, emotional, and physical?

2. What is the difference between "falling in love" and "walking in love"?

3. When it comes to a relationship with another person, what does it mean to "fix your hope on God" rather than on the other person?

4. What are some of the natural consequences of getting the pyramids Chip explained out of order? Give examples.

5. What is the hardest part about making corrections once the process has started incorrectly? What steps would you have to take to make corrections in your life?

Two Models for Lasting Relationships

- The message of society emphasizes the physical and emotional connection first, then the spiritual last.

- God emphasizes the spiritual component first and the physical component as the crowning celebration of intimacy.

ACTION STEPS

Circle the relationship components listed below that have played a role in your current (or most recent) relationship.

Spiritual   Psychological   Physical

Social   Emotional

Which of the components listed above has been the most predominant part of your relationship? Beside each one listed above, place a number (1-5) that ranks them in order. Evaluate the order. Does the order need to change?

Spend some time alone with God in prayer and answer honestly the three questions in the personal evaluation and analysis.

Then,
If you're single, schedule some time with your accountability partner and outline for them the steps you wish to take in "becoming the right person."

If you're dating, set aside some time together to discuss honestly which model you have been following and set goals for how you would like to change.

If you're married, schedule some time with your spouse and outline some ways that you can begin to model God's prescription for your relationship.

AT HOME

It can be difficult to face up to the reality that our relationships aren't in perfect alignment with God's plan. But God is a God of mercy and love, not hardship and denial. When we are willing to take one single step toward Him, we are often amazed at the way He begins to work in our lives. As overwhelming as it may seem to consider revamping your relationship with a significant other, use the space below to describe one step that you need to take this week to begin aligning your love life with God's plan. If you are single, describe one commitment you need to make to yourself to ensure you follow God's approach to falling in love.

MEMORY VERSE

Above all else, guard your heart,
for it is the wellspring of life.
~ Proverbs 4:23 (NIV)

Before You "Fall in Love"

INTRODUCTION

You exchange a quick glance, followed by a warm, inviting smile. The attraction is suddenly intoxicating. Your heart races just a bit. A wonderful, euphoric feeling begins to flood your body, starting in your chest and moving outward to your neck, head, and down to your stomach. Your knees feel strangely weak. In your imagination, you can almost feel the first embrace. You are captivated.

Is it love? Maybe. But most likely it's another phenomenon described in the Bible. And while it shares a close relationship with love, it should never be mistaken for it. In fact, in our culture today, most of our "love baggage" - the heartaches and pains - could be avoided if we simply understood the difference between love and this other phenomenon from Scripture.

In this session, we'll talk about one of the most common pitfalls in romantic relationships today. In addition, we'll discover how to identify the three attributes of true love, and how you can tell if you're really in love. By the end of this session, you'll know the difference between the counterfeits and the real thing. And you'll see why true love makes for a relationship beyond belief.

Video Notes

I. AM I IN LOVE?

_____ This is need love. It is based upon physical attraction and fulfillment. This love is necessary for marriage to succeed; however, marriage cannot be sustained by eros alone.

> [15]Drink water from your own cistern, running water from your own well. [16]Should your springs overflow in the streets, your streams of water in the public squares? [17]Let them be yours alone, never to be shared with strangers. [18]May your fountain be blessed, and may you rejoice in the wife of your youth. [19]A loving doe, a graceful deer- may her breasts satisfy you always, may you ever be captivated by her love. ~ Proverbs 5:15-19 (NIV)

_____ This is friendship love based on reciprocal sharing of time, activities, the home, hobbies, games, and other objects of common affection.

> [9]Love must be sincere. Hate what is evil; cling to what is good. [10]Be devoted to one another in brotherly love. Honor one another above yourselves. [11]Never be lacking in zeal, but keep your spiritual fervor, serving the Lord. [12]Be joyful in hope, patient in affliction, faithful in prayer. [13]Share with God's people who are in need. Practice hospitality. ~ Romans 12:9-13 (NIV)

_____ This is supernatural love. It is giving love and can be unilateral, in that one loves even when the other doesn't respond as expected.

> [4]Love is patient, love is kind. It does not envy, it does not boast, it is not proud. [5]It is not rude, it is not self-seeking, it is not easily angered, it keeps no record of wrongs. [6]Love does not delight in evil but rejoices with the truth. [7]It always protects, always trusts, always hopes, always perseveres. [8]Love never fails. But where there are prophecies, they will cease; where there are tongues, they will be stilled; where there is knowledge, it will pass away.
> ~ 1 Corinthians 13:4-8 (NIV)

Before You "Fall in Love"

II. IS IT LOVE OR INFATUATION?

THE TEST:

Test # 1- _____

Love grows, and all growth requires time. Infatuation may come on suddenly.

Test # 2- _____

Love grows out of an appraisal of all the known characteristics of the other person. Infatuation may arise from an acquaintance with only one or a few of these characteristics.

Test # 3- _____

Love is other-person-centered. It is outgoing. It results in sharing. Infatuation is self-centered.

Test # 4- _____

Genuine love is centered on one person only. An infatuated person may be "in love" with two or more persons simultaneously.

Adapted from *Marriage for Moderns* by Dr. Henry Bowman

"Infatuation is when you think he's as sexy as Robert Redford, as smart as Henry Kissinger, as noble as Ralph Nader, as funny as Woody Allen, and as athletic as Jimmy Conners. Love is when you realize that he's as sexy as Woody Allen, as smart as Jimmy Connors, as funny as Ralph Nader, as athletic as Henry Kissinger and nothing like Robert Redford - but you'll take him anyway."
~ Judith Viorst, Redbook, 1975

Discussion Questions

1. Have you ever been infatuated? Describe.

2. How would you describe the difference between the biblical concept of infatuation and the biblical concept of love?

3. It has been said, "Love is a choice." Is infatuation ever a choice? Explain.

4. Of the first four tests — time, knowledge, focus, and singularity — which one is most important to you?

5. In your most important relationships, to what degree is your attention focused on what you are receiving from them and to what degree is your attention focused on meeting the other's needs?

Before You "Fall in Love"

SESSION 3 KEYS

● Love is different than infatuation.

● There are three attributes in true, biblical love.

● True love is distinguished from infatuation by time, knowledge, focus, and singularity.

ACTION STEPS

For anyone who intends to be romantically involved, it is crucial to understand the difference between love and infatuation. Both can involve such strong emotions that your thinking can become cloudy. How will you tell them apart in your life? In the space below, describe some basic characteristics that you can use to distinguish love from infatuation in the future.

AT HOME

As Proverbs 5:19 demonstrates, it's possible to be infatuated AND be in love. However, infatuation makes it harder to tell if love is the real thing. We've said that true love is distinguished by time, knowledge, focus, and singularity. In the spaces below, create your own criteria that must be met when the real thing comes along.

MY STANDARDS FOR:

Time

Knowledge

Focus

Singularity

MEMORY VERSE

Let her affection fill you at all times with delight,
be infatuated always with her love....
Why should you be infatuated, my son, with a loose
woman and embrace the bosom of an adventuress?
~ Proverbs 5:19-20 (NRSV)

How to Know If You're in Love

INTRODUCTION

As we've already discovered, infatuation is often mistaken for love. But they're not the same. Infatuation is a temporary attraction that is driven predominantly by feelings and physical characteristics. Love is an enduring affection driven by a mature, spiritual choice to be a vessel, sharing God's love with another person.

In this session, we'll explore in deeper detail the different sides of true love. And in the process, we'll discover the important balance that must be present for a lasting relationship between a man and a woman. Love has the potential to create many feelings. But many times, love is simply a choice. And sooner or later, we will all face situations where we are called to give love even though the person doesn't deserve it.

But first, this session picks up where Session Three left off, with the test between love and infatuation.

Video Notes

II. IS IT LOVE OR INFATUATION?

(continued)

Test # 5 - _____

An individual in love tends to have a sense of security and a feeling of trust after considering everything involved in his relationship with the other person. An infatuated individual tends to have a blind sense of security based upon wishful thinking rather than upon careful consideration, or he may have a sense of insecurity that is sometimes expressed as jealousy.

Test # 6 - _____

An individual in love works for the other person or for their mutual benefit. He may study to make the other person proud of him. His ambition is spurred and he plans and saves for the future. He may daydream, but his dreams are reasonably attainable. An infatuated person may lose his ambition, his appetite, his interest in everyday affairs. He thinks of his own misery. He often daydreams, but his dreams are sometimes not limited to the attainable and are given free rein. At times the dreams become substitutes for reality and the individual lives in his world of dreams.

How to Know If You're in Love

Test # 7- _____

A couple in love faces problems frankly and attempts to solve them.
If there are barriers to their getting married, these barriers are approached
intelligently and removed or circumvented. In infatuation, problems tend
to be disregarded or glossed over.

Test # 8- _____

Love tends to be constant.
Infatuation often varies with the distance between the couple.

Test # 9- _____

Physical attraction is a relatively smaller part of their total relationship when
a couple is in love, a relatively greater part when they are infatuated. When a
couple is in love, any physical contact they have tends to have meaning as
well as be a pleasurable experience in and of itself. It tends to express what
they feel toward each other. In infatuation, physical contact tends to be an
end in itself. It represents only pleasurable experience devoid of meaning.

Test # 10- _____

In love, an expression of affection tends to come relatively late in the couple's relationship. In infatuation, it may come earlier, sometimes from the very beginning.

Test # 11- _____

Love tends to endure.
Infatuation may change suddenly, unpredictably.

Test # 12- _____

A couple in love is not indifferent to the effects of postponement of their wedding and do not prolong the period of postponement unless they find it wiser to wait a reasonable time; they do not feel an almost irresistible drive toward haste. Infatuated couples tend to feel an urge toward getting married. Postponement is intolerable to them and they interpret it as deprivation rather than preparation.

Adapted from *Marriage for Moderns* by Dr. Henry Bowman

How to Know If You're in Love

HOW TO DEVELOP YOUR LOVE LIFE

A Picture of Love

_____   Love   _____

_____

A Word to Singles & Involved Couples...

1. Keep your _____ and _____ involvement
   behind your leading from God and commitment to the other person.

A Word to Married Couples...

2. Love requires the nourishment of all three kinds of love.
   Examine which one _____ _____ needs most
   and choose to give it as an act of worship to God.

> "Absence diminishes small loves
> and increases great ones, as the wind blows
> out the candle and fans the bonfire."
> ~ François Duc de La Rochefoucauld

Discussion Questions

1. In the test between love and infatuation, what did you learn about your previous or current relationship? If you identified your relationship as infatuation, which criteria was most helpful?

2. In the pyramid picture of love, which of the three types of love do you think is most important to a marriage? Explain.

3. The three types of love must be in balance for a healthy and lasting relationship. Is there a type of love that has been out of balance in your previous or current relationship?

4. Why is it important to recognize which kind of love the other person needs?

5. A *question for the single*:
   What are some ways you can keep your emotional and physical involvement "behind God's leading"?

   A *question for the married*:
   What is one thing you can do this week that will communicate to your spouse the kind of love that he or she needs?

How to Know If You're in Love

● Love is different from infatuation.

● The three types of love must be in balance for a lasting relationship.

● Your emotional and physical involvement must not surpass God's leading for your relationship.

ACTION STEPS

If you are single, briefly describe your plan to keep your emotional and physical involvement from getting ahead of God's leading in your relationship. Once you have a plan, identify a form of accountability that you can put into practice so that your plan will be successful.

If you are married, identify in the space below which of the three types of love your spouse most needs from you at this time. Describe your plans to give that love this week. At the end of the week, evaluate your success. Then spend time in discussion with your spouse on how to make this a lasting change in your relationship.

Read 2 Samuel 13:1-15.

In verse 15, how would you explain the sudden shift of Amnon's feelings toward Tamar?

Which kind of love had Amnon felt toward her?

*Greater love hath no man than this,
that a man lay down his life for his friends.
~ John 15:13 (KJV)*

Love and Sex: Knowing the Difference Makes All the Difference

INTRODUCTION

Sexual dissatisfaction is one of the fastest growing concerns among married people today. Despite all their dreams of great sex during their married years, many couples consider their sex lives to be a major let-down. Some blame it on poor technique, physical inadequacy, or a lack of interest. But for most of these couples, their sexual disappointment can be traced back to a basic misunderstanding of the relationship between love and sex.

Increasingly today, love and sex are portrayed synonymously. If you're in love, the world suggests, you should also be in bed. In an effort to experience love, many people destroy the thing that was meant to communicate it at the deepest level. If we truly understood the difference between love and sex, it would change our whole perspective on dating and marriage.

There's a direct connection between your current sexual lifestyle and the sex life you will enjoy in the future. Whether you're single or married, the decisions you make today will have a direct impact on the quality of your sexual experiences in the months and years to come. Some people will bear consequences for their choice and others will receive dividends.

In this session, we'll hear from four people as they come face to face with this reality. And through their stories, we'll learn why knowing the difference between love and sex makes all the difference.

Video Notes

A SEA OF DISTORTIONS - FOUR PEOPLE'S STORIES:

Lauren —

Mike —

Paula counseling a woman in her 20s —

Paula counseling a woman in her 30s —

Love and Sex: Knowing the Difference Makes All the Difference

The Lie:

Sex is necessary to keep a growing relationship alive.

THE TRUTH:

Once sex enters into a relationship,
it almost always disintegrates instead of getting better.

The Lie:

If we really love each other, sex is sanctified.

THE TRUTH:

Sex is sanctified only inside the union of biblical marriage.

The Lie:

Having sex is a rite of passage.

THE TRUTH:

With every sexual encounter you diminish the possibility and capacity to experience true intimacy.

THE COMMON THREAD:

They didn't understand the _____ between love and sex.

SUMMARY:

When we fail to understand the difference between love and sex, we are doomed to failure in both our _____ and our _____.

"What is commonly called love, namely the desire of satisfying a voracious appetite with a certain quantity of delicate white human flesh."
~Henry Fielding

"I know nothing about sex, because I was always married."
~Zsa Zsa Gabor

Discussion Questions

1. There were four stories shared during the video segment.
   What are some of the lies the individuals believed about sex?

2. Of all the lies described, which one have you come the closest to believing
   in your life? If you have bought into the lie, how has it impacted your life?

3. How would knowing the difference between love and sex have changed the
   outcomes for:

   Lauren?

   Mike?

   Woman in her 20s?

   Woman in her 30s?

4. How can physical intimacy outside of marriage seem so appealing in one
   moment and cause such pain later on?

5. The Bible tells us that sex apart from total commitment (marriage) produces
   spiritual separation. What does it mean by this?

Love and Sex:
Knowing the Difference
Makes All the Difference

SESSION 5 KEYS

- Distorted thinking usually feels "right" before it makes things go wrong.

- When we fail to understand the difference between love and sex, we are doomed to failure in both our relationships and our sexuality.

ACTION STEPS

It's important to know where you stand on such important issues as love and sex. The crucial decisions in life are never made in the heat of battle. In the space below, describe your beliefs about love and sex, including the standards you intend to uphold in your life.

AT HOME

This week, pay attention to the messages around you - on television, the radio, in the movies, and in conversations at work or with friends. Do you hear any distortions being repeated or reinforced? In the space below, briefly describe some of the attitudes and beliefs that are commonly portrayed in your world. Be prepared to share your findings with the group.

MEMORY VERSE

Flee from sexual immorality.
All other sins a man commits are outside his body, but
he who sins sexually sins against his own body.
~ 1 Corinthians 6:18-19 (NIV)

The Difference Between Love and Sex

INTRODUCTION

There's a profound paradox about sex. It was created to be the ultimate expression of love; and yet, if mishandled, it has the potential to be the ultimate expression of disrespect, selfishness, and degradation. Sex itself is a form of deep, spiritual communication. And it always conveys one of these two, distinctly different messages. It all depends on the context in which it happens.

Your future fulfillment as a sexual being hinges on your understanding of the message sex communicates between you and your partner. Will it be a deep expression of mutual devotion and commitment? Or is it possible that sex, although pleasurable, could be telling your partner that he or she isn't that special at all?

In this session, we'll learn to distinguish love from sex once and for all. We'll see why sometimes the best way to express your love is by having sex; and other times it's by refraining from sex. In addition, we'll discuss how entertaining sexual satisfaction outside the context of marriage reduces your ability to say, "I love you," at the deepest level.

Video Notes

THE CONTEXT

God's Concern for Our Relationships

30And do not grieve the Holy Spirit of God, by whom you were sealed for the day of redemption. 31Let all bitterness and wrath and anger and clamor and slander be put away from you, along with all malice. 32And be kind to one another, tender-hearted, forgiving each other, just as God in Christ also has forgiven you.
~ **Ephesians 4:30-32 (NASB)**

THE COMMAND

Walk in Love!

How?

1. **Positively** - Be giving, caring, sacrificial, and unselfish toward others.

    1Therefore be imitators of God, as beloved children; 2and walk in love, just as Christ also loved you, and gave Himself up for us, an offering and a sacrifice to God as a fragrant aroma. ~ **Ephesians 5:1-2 (NASB)**

2. **Negatively** - Refuse to take, exploit, cheapen, defraud, or substitute sexual activity for genuine love and authentic intimacy.

    3But do not let immorality or any impurity or greed even be named among you, as is proper among saints; 4and no filthiness, silly talk, coarse jesting, which are not fitting, but rather giving of thanks. ~ **Ephesians 5:3-4 (NASB)**

The Difference Between Love and Sex

THE REASON

Sexual Impurity Destroys Relationships

5For this you know with certainty, that no immoral or impure person or covetous man, (who is an idolater), has an inheritance in the kingdom of Christ and God. 6Let no one deceive you with empty words, for because of these things (mentioned above) the wrath of God comes upon the sons of disobedience. ~ **Ephesians 5:5-6 (NASB)**

SPECIFIC APPLICATION

To uninvolved singles: Develop the personal _____ to pursue purity.

To involved singles: Develop a _____ to adopt standards of purity.

To people in crisis: Get _____.

To married people: _____ about it.

To all: *"Come now, let us _____ together," says the LORD. "Though your sins are like scarlet, they shall be as white as snow; though they are red as crimson, they shall be like wool."* ~ **Isaiah 1:18 (NIV)**

> *"There is nothing like early promiscuous sex for dispelling life's bright mysterious expectations."*
> ~Iris Murdoch

Discussion Questions

1. What does obeying and trusting God in the arena of love and sex look like in your life?

2. How would you define sexual immorality? Why is it impossible to be sexually immoral and grow in your relationship with Christ?

3. Why is sex outside of God's boundaries unloving and destructive in relationships?

4. Why is sexual purity so important to God?
   What steps will you take towards sexual purity in the coming week?

5. Read Isaiah 1:18. What does it say about God's love and plans for us?

SESSION 6 The Difference Between Love and Sex

SESSION 6 KEYS

● Sex can either communicate love, or it can communicate disrespect, selfishness, and degradation.

● Sexual immorality destroys relationships.

● Sexual immorality is idolatry-worship of self, not God.

ACTION STEPS

From the video notes, which of the Specific Application points most applies to your situation? In the space below, briefly describe how you will take the prescribed action this week.

AT HOME

Sometimes it's hard to believe that God would reserve sex for marriage while not approving it for unmarried couples who truly love each other. Does it really matter that much? Is there something magical about the wedding ceremony ... or the marriage license? This week, read Ephesians 5:1-6 again on your own. Then in the space below, write your own explanation of how sex should relate to love and marriage.

MEMORY VERSE

But immorality or any impurity or greed must not even be named among you, as is proper among saints;
~ Ephesians 5:3 (NASB)

Sexual Purity in a Sex-Saturated World

INTRODUCTION

The pull of sex is one of the strongest forces in nature. In fact, statistics show that sexual immorality is virtually the same between church-going and unchurched groups. Despite the fact that they believe it's wrong, many people who consider themselves Christians are powerless when it comes to resisting the intoxicating power of sex.

The same is true for you. Even if you have a desire to pursue sexual purity for your life, that's not enough. Despite your intentions and your sincerity, you need something more if it is to become a reality.

But don't despair. You can achieve a level of sexual purity that pleases God and ensures His best blessings on your relationships in the future. The Bible gives clear instructions for living out God's standards for sex — whether you're single or married. In this session, we'll discover why loving relationships demand sexual purity.

Video Notes

FIVE FACTS ABOUT SEX

1. Those who abstain from sexual intercourse before marriage report the _____ levels of sexual satisfaction in marriage.

2. Those who cohabitate before marriage have a 50% higher rate of _____ than those who do not.

3. Those who cohabitate are more likely to experience _____ in marriage.

4. The introduction of sex into a dating relationship almost always ushers in the _____ of the relationship.

5. Sexually-transmitted diseases, including AIDS, can remain _____ for up to a decade or more but can be passed on to others during that time.

HOW TO SAY "YES" TO LOVE AND "NO" TO SECOND-RATE SEX

I. Loving relationships demand sexual _____.

THE COMMAND

Refrain from sexual immorality.

> [2] and walk in love, just as Christ also loved you and gave Himself up for us, an offering and a sacrifice to God as a fragrant aroma. [3] But immorality or any impurity or greed must not even be named among you, as is proper among saints; [4] and there must be no filthiness and silly talk, or coarse jesting, which are not fitting, but rather giving of thanks.
> ~ Ephesians 5:2-4 (NASB)

Sexual Purity in a Sex-Saturated World

THE REASON

He (God) loves you.

> [5]For this you know with certainty, that no immoral or impure person or covetous man, who is an idolater, has an inheritance in the kingdom of Christ and God. [6]Let no one deceive you with empty words, for because of these things the wrath of God comes upon the sons of disobedience. ~ Ephesians 5:5-6 (NASB)

THE APPLICATION

Do not participate in sin, for you are brand-new in Christ.

> [7]Therefore do not be partakers with them; [8]for you were formerly darkness, but now you are Light in the Lord; walk as children of Light [9](for the fruit of the Light consists in all **goodness** and **righteousness** and **truth**), [10]trying to learn what is pleasing to the Lord. ~ Ephesians 5:7-10 (NASB)

HOW TO SAY "YES" TO LOVE AND "NO" TO SECOND-RATE SEX

I. Loving relationships demand sexual purity.

II. Sexual purity demands a game plan.

(to be continued...)

> "Whoever is in a hurry shows
> that the thing he is about is too big for him."
> ~ Lord Chesterfield

Discussion Questions

1. Does the fact that premarital and extramarital sex are "taboo" make them more appealing? Why or why not?

2. What are some examples of rules that you're glad exist?

3. Why do you think the idea of delayed gratification motivates some people but not others?

4. Outside of marriage, how far is "too far"? Why?

5. Which of God's rules about sex feels the most restricting to you? Why?

Sexual Purity in a Sex-Saturated World

SESSION 7 KEYS

- Every gift that flows out of love almost always comes with rules.

- God's rules for sex always maximize our pleasure in the long run.

- Loving relationships demand sexual purity.

ACTION STEPS

Read Ephesians 5:7-12. According to this passage, how far should you go to ensure that you are not a "partaker" of immorality? What would this look like in your life? After reading the Scripture and pondering the questions, spend some time in prayer. Ask God to show the appropriate boundaries for your relationships (current or future). Be prepared to share your boundaries with a trusted friend or accountability partner.

AT HOME

The purpose of God's rules about sex is to maximize your relationships in the future. Read Romans 12:2. What is one thing you can do now to take a step toward greater purity and maximize your relationships?

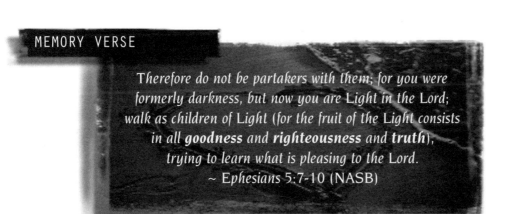

MEMORY VERSE

*Therefore do not be partakers with them; for you were formerly darkness, but now you are Light in the Lord; walk as children of Light (for the fruit of the Light consists in all **goodness** and **righteousness** and **truth**), trying to learn what is pleasing to the Lord.*
~ Ephesians 5:7-10 (NASB)

How to Say "Yes" to Love and "No" to Second-Rate Sex

INTRODUCTION

There's something about rules that seems to take the fun out of everything. Since the time of Adam and Eve, men and women have had a hard time accepting rules without testing them first. When something is off limits, somehow it becomes all the more attractive to the human spirit.

And yet, beneath it all, rules are crucial to our happiness, safety, and survival. The rules in a sporting event enable us to enjoy the competition, while the rules of the road keep us from certain disaster. Like them or not, rules are meant to maximize our long-term enjoyment.

The rules of sex are no different. God made rules about sex, not for our misery, but for our benefit. In this session, we'll examine specific evidence of the benefits of following these rules…and the consequences of breaking them. And we'll see, that although we may not understand the connection at first, following God's rules for sex always maximizes our pleasure in the long run. In this session, we'll discover a strategy for saying "Yes" to love and "No" to second-rate sex.

Video Notes

HOW TO SAY "YES" TO LOVE AND "NO" TO SECOND-RATE SEX

I. Loving relationships demand sexual _____.

II. Sexual purity demands a _____ _____.

    1. Develop _____.
    Purity requires a personal commitment to the truth. (Ephesians 5:2-4)

    2. Ponder the _____.
    Fear can be a legitimate and healthy motivator for delayed gratification.
    (Ephesians 5:5-6)

    3. Make _____.
    Advanced decision making is an absolute necessity for sexual purity.
    (Ephesians 5:7-9)

> *Run from anything that stimulates youthful lust. Follow anything that makes you want to do right. Pursue faith and love and peace, and enjoy the companionship of those who call on the Lord with pure hearts.* ~ **2 Timothy** 2:22 **(TLB)**

    4. Get _____.
    Asking others to help you keep your commitments to God will empower
    you to walk "pleasing to the Lord." (Ephesians 5:10)

> *And do not be conformed to this world, but be transformed by the renewing of your mind, so that you may prove what the will of God is, that which is good and acceptable and perfect.* ~ **Romans** 12:2 **(NASB)**

III. Sexual Purity's Pay Off is Awesome!

    1. God's way _____!

    2. It's never too _____!

    3. A word to virgins: you are not _____, you are wise!

"What matters is not the idea a man holds,
but the depth at which he holds it."
~ Ezra Pound

Discussion Questions

1. In your own words, what is the difference between belief and conviction?
   In what areas of your life do you need to convert your beliefs to convictions?

2. How can fear be a legitimate and healthy motivator for sexual purity?

3. How does your perception of a person change after learning that he or she
   is a virgin?

4. What specific pre-decisions are you going to make to help you win your
   battle for sexual purity?

5. Who is the person that can help you develop a game plan and hold you
   accountable to your commitment to God? What would your game plan need
   to include?

SESSION 8 KEYS

- Sexual purity demands a game plan.

- Get accountability!

- It's never too late to become sexually pure.

ACTION STEPS

Take Chip up on his challenge. Spend some time alone with God this week. Seek His guidance as you determine your personal convictions for staying sexually pure. Then take a moment to ponder the consequences. Finally, make a list of your pre-decisions.

AT HOME

Accountability is perhaps the most important key to success against temptation. It can also be one of the most intimidating to pursue. This week, prayerfully consider sharing your list of pre-decisions with one or two trustworthy believers. Even if your attempts to reach out feel a bit awkward, the rewards can be priceless!

MEMORY VERSE

Run from anything that gives you the evil thoughts that young men often have, but stay close to anything that makes you want to do right. Have faith and love, and enjoy the companionship of those who love the Lord and have pure hearts.
~ 2 Timothy 2:22 (TLB)

Wake Up World! There's a Better Way to Do Relationships

INTRODUCTION

Hollywood suggests that successful relationships are built on finding the right person, falling in love, and fixing your hopes and dreams of future fulfillment on that person. But relationships aren't working, marriages are failing, and we're left wondering "Why?"

If you ask me, something seems to be missing. Something is wrong. So where do we turn for answers to this complex issue?

God has a plan. He has given us a revolutionary way to build relationships with the opposite sex — a way that honors the other person, a way built on love, not lust, a way that results in deeper intimacy and long-term commitment.

Join me in this next session and learn why God wants to give you His very best in your relationships!

**Wake Up World!
There's a Better Way
to Do Relationships**

SESSION 9

Video Notes

CHIP'S STORY

"A Norman Rockwell Picture"

27 years ago… A small farmhouse in the country… A young couple beginning God's journey together… An ordinary moment with extraordinary impact…

A "_____" that changed my life

CHIP'S REALIZATION

"God sets boundaries because He wants to give you His very best."

He who did not spare his own Son, but gave him up for us all-how will he not also, along with him, graciously give us all things? ~ **Romans 8:32 (NIV)**

CHIP'S EPIPHANY

"I am going to do life God's way."

Where there is no revelation, the people cast off restraint; but blessed is he who keeps the law.
~ **Proverbs 29:18 (NIV)**

Wake Up World! There's a Better Way to Do Relationships

WHY IS SEX SUCH SERIOUS BUSINESS TO GOD?

Ephesians 5:11-14

The Command =

And do not participate in the unfruitful deeds of darkness,
but instead even expose them;
verse 11

The Reason =

. . . for it is disgraceful even to speak of the things
which are done by them in secret.
verse 12

The Explanation =

But all things become visible when they are exposed by the light,
for everything that becomes visible is light.
verse 13

The Invitation =

For this reason it says, 'Awake, sleeper, and arise from the dead,
and Christ will shine on you.'
verse 14

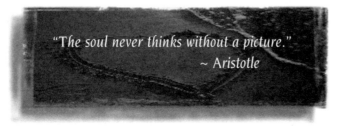

"The soul never thinks without a picture."
~ Aristotle

Wake Up World!
There's a Better Way
to Do Relationships

SESSION 9

Discussion Questions

1. Why is sex such serious business to God? What is at stake for the world around us?

2. Chip described the time he got a vision for the type of family life he wanted. Describe your vision for the family and relationship you've always dreamed of.

3. Sexual immorality so violates God's holy character that He tells us not to even speak about it. What does Chip suggest is more powerful than our words?

4. What does Chip mean when he says that your life is a "light"? How can you be an ambassador to pass it on?

5. What would happen if God's church said, "Let's get radical!"? What changes would you need to make in your life to be part of the "second sexual revolution"?

Wake Up World!
There's a Better Way to Do Relationships

- Sex is serious business to God.

- All things become visible when they are exposed by the light.

- We are to expose the world's destructive attitude toward sex, not by what we say, but by how we live.

ACTION STEPS

Set aside some time this week and rate yourself on scale of one to ten. How would you rank your own sexual purity in mind, word, and deed? Write a sentence or two to explain your answer for each.

Wake Up World! There's a Better Way to Do Relationships

SESSION 9

AT HOME

Remembering that night in a little farmhouse, Chip basked in the glow of a pure and loving relationship and for the first time saw sexual purity the way God sees it. The light exposed his distorted view of sex and his twisted view of relationships. In that defining moment Chip decided "I'm going to live my life God's way."

Have you ever had a moment like that where God spoke into your life so clearly? Take some time this week and evaluate the defining moments of your life. How did you respond to the call to change?

MEMORY VERSE

Where there is no revelation,
the people cast off restraint;
but blessed is he who keeps the law.
~ Proverbs 29:18 (NASB)

The Second Sexual Revolution

INTRODUCTION

Great ideas can spread like wildfire. And all it takes to get it started is a spark of light. In fact, the Bible explains that God's ideas spread the way light emanates from a light source - penetrating the darkness and making all things bright.

God's ideas about sex are great ideas. As you embrace them in your own life, you, in turn, become a light source to pass them on to others. Can you imagine a world dominated by the truth about sex? What if TV, music, and the movies no longer repeated distortions about sex and relationships? What if they began to reflect God's view instead?

It's possible. As we'll see in this final session, all it takes is a very small percentage of faithful people who are serious about doing sex God's way. It's not a matter of judging and condemning other sinners. It just means being brave enough to take a stand against the status quo and live out your beliefs in a way that goes against the current — a revolutionary approach to love, sex, and lasting relationships.

Video Notes

ANATOMY OF A SEXUAL REVOLUTION

I. A revolutionary way to _____ about human sexuality.

    1. Sex is _____ —

    2. Sex is _____ —

[15]Do you not know that your bodies are members of Christ? Shall I then take away the members of Christ and make them members of a prostitute? May it never be! [16]Or do you not know that the one who joins himself to a prostitute is one body with her? For He says, "THE TWO SHALL BECOME ONE FLESH." [17]But the one who joins himself to the Lord is one spirit with Him. [18]Flee immorality. Every other sin that a man commits is outside the body, but the immoral man sins against his own body. [19]Or do you not know that your body is a temple of the Holy Spirit who is in you, whom you have from God, and that you are not your own? [20]For you have been bought with a price: therefore glorify God in your body. ~ 1 Corinthians 6:15-20 (NASB)

Marriage is to be held in honor among all, and the marriage bed is to be undefiled; for fornicators and adulterers God will judge. ~ Hebrews 13:4 (NASB)

II. A revolutionary way to _____ the opposite sex.

[3]Your adornment must not be merely external-braiding the hair, and wearing gold jewelry, or putting on dresses; [4]but let it be the hidden person of the heart, with the imperishable quality of a gentle and quiet spirit, which is precious in the sight of God. ~1 Peter 3:3-4 (NASB)

    I _____ Character

    O _____ Modesty

    U _____ Devotion

The Second Sexual Revolution

III. A revolutionary way to _____ to the opposite sex.

   1. As a _____.

      Greater love has no one than this, that one lay down his life for his friends.
      ~ John 15:13 (NASB)

   2. As a _____ member.

      [1]Do not sharply rebuke an older man, but rather appeal to him as a father, to the younger men as brothers, [2]the older women as mothers, and the younger women as sisters, in all purity. ~1 Timothy 5:1-2 (NASB)

   3. As fellow _____ ____ _____.

      [24]and let us consider how to stimulate one another to love and good deeds, [25]not forsaking our own assembling together, as is the habit of some, but encouraging one another; and all the more as you see the day drawing near.
      ~ Hebrews 10:24-25 (NASB)

> *"Revolutions are not made; they come.*
> *A revolution is as natural as an oak tree.*
> *It comes out of the past;*
> *its foundations are laid far back."*
> *~ Wendell Phillips*

Discussion Questions

1. Is the time right to start a revolution? Why or why not?
   In your opinion, what does it take to start a revolution?

2. In what ways do you need to change how you think about sex?
   What implications does this have on your thought life? Behavior?
   Viewing habits? Renewing of your mind?

3. How does modesty facilitate loving and lasting relationships?
   In what ways has our culture seduced us into attracting the opposite sex
   in ways that focus on outer versus inner qualities?

4. Is it possible that the whole "dating paradigm" is not the wisest or most
   effective way to build relationships with the opposite sex? Explain.

5. How could you answer God's call to the "Second Sexual Revolution"?
   What might that look like in your life and relationships?

The Second Sexual Revolution

SESSION 10 KEYS

- Revolution means a new way to think about human sexuality.

- Revolution means a new way to attract the opposite sex.

- Revolution means a new way to relate to the opposite sex.

ACTION STEPS

This week, start a personal revolution by committing to a new approach to the opposite sex. In the spaces below, describe how you will think about, attract, and relate to the opposite sex. Give specific examples for each.

THINK ABOUT:

ATTRACT:

RELATE TO:

AT HOME

Are you ready to take a radical step of faith and believe God's Word that:

1. Sex is sacred
2. Sex is serious
3. Sex is an awesome responsibility

In what specific ways do you need to change your way of thinking in order to become part of the second sexual revolution?

We need a countercultural movement among Christians to let God's light shine. After you've spent some time in the Word and in prayer, I encourage you to put what you've experienced in the last 10 sessions in to practice. Turn the page, follow the outline, and make a personal covenant with your Father. He loves you, He's for you, and He wants to give you His best. I invite you to join me in answering God's call to a second sexual revolution!

MEMORY VERSE

And let not your adornment be merely external-braiding the hair, and wearing gold jewelry, or putting on dresses; but let it be the hidden person of the heart, with the imperishable quality of a gentle and quiet spirit, which is precious in the sight of God.
~ 1 Peter 3:3-4 (NASB)

Heavenly Father,

Thank you for your Word in Ephesians that teaches me how to love as you would have me to do so. Thank you that the same power that raised Christ from the dead lives in me and enables me to be pure. Help me to think differently about my sexuality, to attract others with integrity and honesty, and to relate in truthful and helpful ways to those around me.

From this day forward I will be sexually pure. Give me your strength to become the right person, to grow and walk in love, and to fix my hope on you, walking in your light. Give me the courage to be radical in my faith and allow me to make a difference as I commit to be a part of the second sexual revolution.

Amen.

My pre-decisions for sexual purity are:

1.

2.

3.

My game plan for sexual purity is:

1.

2.

3.

My accountability partners are:

1.

2.

I want to become a part of the second sexual revolution
and choose not simply to talk about my faith, but to live it out.

_____   _____

Name   Date

Welcome to the Revolution

by Chip Ingram

Dear Friends,

As the old song says "It only takes a spark to get a fire going" and the fact of the matter is, it's true! So how about you? Are you ready for the second sexual revolution? Will you join me?

Learning this material may be a great first step, but revolutions occur when there is a movement. Movements occur when people go beyond themselves and become committed to taking it to the next level of impact.

My question for you, as you finish this series is: *"How will you take what you've learned in this series and "pass it on" to your circle of influence?"*

Many people have already completed *Love, Sex & Lasting Relationships* and have now launched it successfully in their high school, college, singles group, or small groups in their church.

I encourage you to share what you've learned with those in your network of friends. If you have a testimony of how this study has impacted your life, I'd love to hear from you. You can email me at therevolution@walkthru.org.

Keep Pressin' Ahead,

THE TOOLS FOR THIS SERIES

Walk Thru the Bible has prepared a comprehensive course to bring the principles of this series alive in each participant's life. Your job is to guide your group through the study sessions and the exercises, allowing them to discover the concepts, embrace their meaning, and apply them to their lives.

Love, Sex & Lasting Relationships is intended to be more than just a course. It is a 10-week experience that will equip the people in your group to experience God's design for intimacy with the opposite sex. This kit contains:

Ten **Video** sessions featuring the teaching of Chip Ingram.

A **Course Workbook** designed to help each participant personalize the lessons. Complete with: Video Notes with a fill-in-the-blank outline for taking notes during each of the video sessions; penetrating Group Discussion Questions that correspond with each lesson; and life-changing exercises to implement the lessons into everyday life.

The video sessions and the workbook are designed to create a learning experience that equips participants not only to understand God's design for relationships, but also to begin applying those principles right away. (To order extra materials for *Love, Sex & Lasting Relationships*, call Walk Thru the Bible at 1-800-763-5433.)

Leading Your Group Through Love, Sex and Lasting Relationships

GETTING STARTED - 5 EASY STEPS

Several basic ingredients are essential to any successful group study.
Before you plan the first meeting, you should work through these fundamentals.

1. First, pray! Only God can change the hearts of men, and prayer is your most powerful tool. As the leader of your group, this is your logical starting place.

2. Next, organize. Consider asking one or two others to share the leadership load by helping you plan, promote the series, distribute materials, etc.

3. Order the Course Workbooks. Before starting the course, make sure that each participant has his own copy of the Course Workbook. You may want to have extra copies on hand to accommodate any late additions to your group. This series is designed to be highly interactive, and the Course Workbook is essential for integrating the principles into daily life.

   (If your sponsoring organization is not underwriting the cost of materials, then consider structuring your class so that the Course Workbook is part of a registration fee for the series.)

4. Encourage attendance. Walk Thru the Bible has promotional materials such as posters and bulletin inserts available to help you announce this series and encourage your participants to attend. (Call 1-800-763-5433 for more information.)

5. Prepare to lead the sessions. In the following pages of this Leader's Guide, you will find a Session Guide for each of the ten Video Sessions. Each one contains guidelines for the class, discussion questions, and tips. You can keep the Session Guide with you during your group time, to help you lead each session with confidence!

Things to Remember While Leading This Series

TRIED AND TRUE TIPS FOR THE SUCCESSFUL VIDEO SERIES LEADER

● Cover The Material:

Of all the things you do as the leader of this series, your main objective is to work through each Video Session and cover the discussion questions with your group in the allotted time. Each of the ten video lessons is accompanied by important discussion questions, exercises, and Scriptures. There's a lot of searching and growing to be done between lessons, and it all builds on the content of the video and the discussion questions. It is STRONGLY RECOMMENDED that you view one session at a time, in order for the rest of the materials to have their full effect.

● Let The Teacher Teach:

Chip Ingram is the "expert" in this series. For over thirty years he has been studying Scripture, counseling, and exploring the issues surrounding love and sex in relationships. Since he brings his expertise to every session, you can sit back and relax while he presents the material. Your expertise is needed in facilitating his teaching and cultivating good conversation during the discussion time. The Leader's Guide and the Course Workbook will prove to be helpful for you as the facilitator.

● Be Yourself:

The others in your group will appreciate and follow your example of openness and honesty as you lead - so set a good example! The best way to encourage those in your class is not to impress them with your own wisdom, but with your sincere desire to live out these principles in your own life. When they sense that you are "real" - that you are not "above" the issues that challenge them - they will be encouraged to press on. Someone who struggles with sexual purity needs encouragement to overcome the challenges. The transparency of your group may be the crucial ingredient that sparks their motivation.

● *Be Prepared:*

Hopefully, the discussion questions will raise some interesting conversation in your group. However, you can also lose focus during discussion time as people present opinions that may detract from the focus of the lesson, or may not represent biblical teaching. A good way to keep things on track is to point the conversation back to a related point that is covered in the *Love, Sex & Lasting Relationships* materials. But that can only happen if you are familiar with the lessons. If you will be the leader throughout the entire series, Walk Thru the Bible recommends that you view all of the video sessions before beginning your series. If the participants will be taking turns leading each week, this is not necessary. In many cases, your familiarity with the series content can help you keep things headed in the desired direction at all times.

ABOUT YOUR VIDEO TEACHER

Chip Ingram is your teacher for *Love, Sex & Lasting Relationships*. Chip Ingram is the teaching pastor of the Living on the Edge radio ministry and the president and chief executive officer of Walk Thru the Bible Ministries. Chip's successful radio program, which began in 1995, has expanded to nearly 700 stations nationwide. A graduate of Dallas Theological Seminary, Chip has a unique ability to communicate biblical truth in a way that brings about transformation in lives. He is also the father of four grown children.

HOW TO STRUCTURE YOUR GROUP TIME

Whether you are leading this series in Sunday School or a small group Bible Study, you'll find the materials are ideal for most small group settings. The course is designed so that the video teaching and the discussion questions will fit into an hour segment. Of course, you can take extra time for discussion or to review the previous week's material if time permits. Whatever your time frame, be sure that your group views one new video lesson per week, and that they complete their homework assignments between meetings.

Below is the suggested way to use these materials.

IN CLASS

1. *Video Class Notes:*

Each video session has a corresponding section in the Course Workbook for participants to follow along as Chip teaches. A numbered, fill-in-the-blank outline highlights the main points of the video, and there is room for additional notes and insights as well. The "answers" to the notes can be found in the Leader's Guide for each session.

2. *Discussion Questions:*

The Course Workbook also contains discussion questions for each of the video sessions. They are designed to help your participants personalize the content of each lesson. You can move right to these questions immediately after the conclusion of the video.

VERY IMPORTANT: The main goal of these questions is to help you stir up discussion in your group. Encourage your group to answer with more than short "yes" and "no" answers. Use the questions to draw people into discussing their hearts, their struggles, and how the teaching could be applied to their personal situations.

Things to Remember While Leading This Series

3. Action Steps:

The Course Workbook then moves into specific action steps that are designed to help create specific ways to apply the material. Your group will benefit tremendously by sharing ideas and discussing the recommended action steps together. Some of the best discussion time comes from this segment. Be sure to be honest and transparent during this time. Make it clear that you are a fellow learner, not an untouchable "expert" on the Bible and relationships. Make your group a safe environment for sharing personal struggles. Together, your group can minister to each other, helping to apply God's word to everyday situations.

AFTER CLASS

4. At Home:

These in-depth, personal studies are intended to motivate the students to take the principles right off the page and into their lives. This is where the series moves from contemplation to application. As the participants immerse themselves in these materials each day, the transformation process begins. Urge the people in your group to complete their assignments weekly. Insist on it! You may even want to include a brief review of their home work at the designated point near the end of each week's group discussion.

SUGGESTED FORMAT

1. View the Video Lesson, filling in the notes in the Course Workbook
   (25-35 minutes)

2. Review the Discussion Questions
   (20 minutes)

3. Clarify assignment for upcoming week
   (5 minutes)

4. Prayer requests, group prayer
   (10 minutes)

Leader's Guide Session Notes

SESSION 1

HOLLYWOOD'S FORMULA FOR LASTING RELATIONSHIPS

Key Point:

We live in a world in which love is portrayed on TV, in movies, and in music. But the perspective reinforced by these media messages is in stark contrast to what the Bible teaches about love, sex, and lasting relationships. To understand this issue, we must first recognize the difference between these two sources of information, as well as the impact each is having in shaping our thinking.

Video Notes
Answer Key:

I. HOLLYWOOD'S PRESCRIPTION FOR LASTING RELATIONSHIPS:

1. <u>FIND</u> the right person.
2. <u>FALL</u> in love.
3. <u>FIX</u> your hopes and dreams of future fulfillment on that person.
4. If <u>FAILURE</u> occurs, repeat steps 1, 2, and 3.

II. GOD'S PRESCRIPTION FOR LASTING RELATIONSHIPS:

1. <u>BECOME</u> the right person.
2. <u>WALK</u> in love.
3. <u>FIX</u> your hope on God and seek to please Him through this relationship.

Notes for Discussion Questions:

1. Give some examples of popular movies, music, television, magazines, etc. that sell Hollywood's prescription for lasting relationships.

   This is the first group discussion time for your group. The main goal at this point is to get the people in your group to open up and share. The best way to do that is to model informal conversation. If no one volunteers to share their thoughts, start by sharing your own. Keep the bar very low at first. Share a very simple observation that requires no deep thought. You might offer something as trivial as, "I used to have a shirt just like the one Chip was wearing in this session." The point is — build relationships with your group! Even if you do not struggle with love, sex, or relationships, it is in your group's best interest that you demonstrate some transparency and self-criticism by finding something that tells your group that it's okay not to be perfect. You may simply say, "I need to pay more attention to the messages that are around me." If you can't think of anything you'd improve, then you should say, "My biggest problem is recognizing my blind spots!" Avoid leading off with a "profound" insight. It might intimidate some of your fellow students. If you shut them down at the start, it may be very difficult to get them to open up later.

2. How have the things you watch, read, and listen to shaped what you believe about love and sex? In what ways have you bought into Hollywood's prescription for lasting relationships?

This can be a compelling question with arguments on both sides. It is intended to stir opinions among the participants in your group.

3. In your pursuit of a lasting relationship, have you been more focused on finding someone, or on becoming someone? What was your result?

The questions in this series are designed to move gradually from general information to personal introspection. This question invites participants to examine their own default philosophies on love and relationships.

4. Which is easier: to become an imitator of God or an imitator of a Hollywood role model? Explain.

There are no right or wrong answers here. The purpose of this question is to expose the power of the role models in our lives.

5. Of all the qualities you look for in a mate, which ones do you think will be the most important to you long term? Do you possess these qualities? If not, what will you do this week in your pursuit to "become the right person"?

Throughout this series, it will be important to develop a vision for the type of relationship that is desirable. This question is the first effort toward that goal.

ACTION STEPS

When we examine the source of our beliefs, the findings can be astounding. Rather than coming from Scripture or sound teaching, many of our assumptions about love, sex, and relationships come from less credible sources.

AT HOME

The only way to correct the wrong thinking from our past is by transforming our minds to God's Truth. This exercise models out the process of systematically replacing the distortions in our thinking with God's wisdom on the issues.

SESSION 2

TWO MODELS FOR LASTING RELATIONSHIPS

Key Point:

The pervasive approach to love in our culture is, in fact, the exact opposite of how God's Word advises us to approach it. This session clearly outlines the priorities Scripture says we should maintain when pursuing love.

Video Notes

Answer Key:

GOD'S PROCESS FOR FALLING IN LOVE

1. Ask: Is this person a committed <u>BELIEVER</u>?
2. Observe the person <u>SOCIALLY</u>.
3. Get to <u>KNOW</u> each other.
4. Keep your emotions behind <u>GOD'S</u> lead.
5. Come together <u>PHYSICALLY</u>.

Leader's Guide Session Notes

Notes for Discussion Questions:

1. How successful has your current approach been in developing and sustaining long-term, healthy relationships that include all areas of intimacy — the spiritual, emotional, and physical?

   This question is intended to prompt self-examination of our own approach to relationships.

2. What is the difference between "falling in love" and "walking in love"?

   Revisiting these differences from the video message will help participants to understand the fallacy of "falling in love" and the importance of "walking in love."

3. When it comes to a relationship with another person, what does it mean to "fix your hope on God" rather than on the other person?

   Life is a process of learning dependence on God. Love is yet another arena in which we must learn to rely on God rather than on the things that comprise our circumstances.

4. What are some of the natural consequences of getting the process explained in the triangles out of order? Give examples.

   This question is designed to create a "felt need" with participants in which they connect their behavior with certain benefits and consequences.

5. What is the hardest part about making corrections once the process has started incorrectly? What steps would you have to take to make corrections in your life?

   Momentum plays a huge role in keeping people trapped in negative relationship patterns. This question helps participants begin getting to the bottom of what is required to bring about change.

ACTION STEPS

When we analyze our priorities in developing a relationship, it can be eye-opening. This exercise helps to imply the importance of becoming intentional to pursue relationships with the right priorities in mind.

AT HOME

It can be very difficult for someone to change his entire approach to relationships. However, for many people, that is what will be required. The purpose of this exercise is to encourage the people in your group to begin strategizing how they can be obedient to turn to God and begin pursuing His design for love — no matter what the cost.

SESSION 3

BEFORE YOU "FALL IN LOVE"

Key Point:

The primary confusion in our culture is that a phenomenon known as infatuation is commonly mistaken for love. As a result, love is one of the least understood terms today. This session sheds light on both love and infatuation, and the legitimate role of each one in our lives.

Video Notes

Answer Key:

AM I IN LOVE?

EROS – This is need love.

PHILEO – This is friendship love.

AGAPE – This is giving love.

IS IT LOVE OR INFATUATION?

TEST # 1: TIME

TEST # 2: KNOWLEDGE

TEST # 3: FOCUS

TEST # 4: SINGULARITY

Leader's Guide Session Notes

Notes for Discussion Questions:

1. Have you ever been infatuated? Describe. How long did it last?

   Virtually everyone has experienced infatuation. Encourage everyone to revisit their feelings and to compare them to the biblical concept of love.

2. How would you describe the difference between the biblical concept of infatuation and the biblical concept of love?

   In light of the previous question, participants should now be able to take the next step and clarify the distinction between love and infatuation. By doing so, they will be more equipped to recognize and understand each one when they experience them in the future.

3. It has been said, "Love is a choice." Is infatuation ever a choice? Explain.

   Infatuation is an involuntary response. However, it only happens when we make ourselves mentally available to it. Furthermore, it is cultivated and intensified when we entertain the feelings. By making intentional choices about your standards about friendships and a spouse, it is possible to avoid becoming infatuated with a person that doesn't meet your criteria for a long-term relationship.

4. Of the first four tests — time, knowledge, focus, and singularity — which one is most important to you?

   This question will help participants begin to make application of the content of this session. As the leader, encourage group members to examine why this test is especially important in his or her life. It is helpful to think about past experiences, as well as look ahead at the kind of relationship you desire to have.

5. In your most important relationships, to what degree is your attention focused on what you are receiving from them and to what degree is your attention focused on meeting the other's needs?

   The purpose of this question is to prompt participants to examine their perspectives on relationships. This is a good opportunity to revisit the importance of agape love.

ACTION STEPS

The purpose of this exercise is to give participants a chance to describe, in their own words, the differences between love and infatuation. By personalizing the essence of this week's session, they will be better equipped to pursue lasting relationships in the future.

AT HOME

Similar to the Action Steps above, this exercise will prompt the people in your group to make a personalized statement of their intentions for recognizing acceptable relationships in the future.

SESSION 4

HOW TO KNOW IF YOU'RE IN LOVE

Key Point:

Unlike infatuation, love often comes down to a choice — will I show love to this person even though he or she doesn't deserve it? More than any other, this distinction helps to separate true love from the images of love often portrayed in the media.

Video Notes
Answer Key:

IS IT LOVE OR INFATUATION? (CONTINUED)

TEST #5: <u>SECURITY</u>

TEST #6: <u>WORK</u>

TEST #7: <u>PROBLEM-SOLVING</u>

TEST #8: <u>DISTANCE</u>

TEST #9: <u>PHYSICAL ATTRACTION AND INVOLVEMENT</u>

TEST #10: <u>AFFECTION</u>

TEST #11: <u>STABILITY</u>

TEST #12: <u>DELAYED GRATIFICATION</u>

HOW TO DEVELOP YOUR LOVE LIFE

1. Keep your <u>EMOTIONAL</u> and <u>PHYSICAL</u> involvement behind your leading from God and commitment to the other person.
2. Love requires the nourishment of all three kinds of love. Examine which one <u>YOUR</u> <u>MATE</u> needs most and choose to give it as an act of worship to God.

Notes for Discussion Questions:

1. In the test between love and infatuation, which criteria were most helpful? Why?

   The purpose of this question is simply to generate discussion in which people can share their personal reactions to the video message.

2. In the triangle picture of love, which of the three types of love do you think is most important to a marriage? Explain.

   Group members should conclude that agape love, sooner or later, is the type of love that holds a relationship together.

3. The three types of love must be in balance for a healthy and lasting relationship. Is there a type of love that has been out of balance in your previous or current relationship?

   This question is intended simply to prompt participants to examine how this principle applies to their own relationships. It is helpful for participants to look at this question from both perspectives: what type of love have you been missing, and what type of love your mate may have been lacking from you?

4. Why is it important to recognize which kind of love the other person needs?

   The nature of love is to meet the other person's needs. Many people mistakenly pursue love without recognizing this principle; instead, they often pursue love based on how it serves their own needs.

5. A *question for the single*:

> What are some ways you can keep your emotional and physical involvement "behind God's leading"?

A *question for the married*:

> What is one thing you can do this week that will communicate to your spouse the kind of love that he or she needs?

> *These questions are important to answer personally, but should also encourage discussion when directed to a group. Encourage members to be authentic and realistic and to hold one another accountable.*

> *Both of these questions are designed to produce action steps that can be applied this week from the material in the session.*

ACTION STEPS

This is an important exercise that will lead to each participant to take important steps this week in accordance with his or her situation in life.

AT HOME

A study of the story between Amnon and Tamar provides rich insight into the difference between love and infatuation, as well as the consequences of allowing infatuation to drive your decisions about love and sex. The love Amnon felt toward Tamar was only eros. Because he lacked phileo and agape love for Tamar, we can conclude that it was not love, but was merely infatuation.

Leader's Guide Session Notes

SESSION 5

LOVE AND SEX: KNOWING THE DIFFERENCE MAKES ALL THE DIFFERENCE

Key Point:

This session reveals the consequences of making wrong choices about sex. In addition, it examines several common lies that lead to those destructive decisions. The conclusion of the discussion is that when we fail to understand the difference between love and sex, we are doomed to failure in both our relationships and our sexuality.

Video Notes

Answer Key:

THE COMMON THREAD

1. They didn't understand the <u>DIFFERENCE</u> between love and sex.

SUMMARY

2. When we fail to understand the difference between love and sex, we are doomed to failure in both our <u>RELATIONSHIPS</u> and our <u>SEXUALITY</u>.

Notes for Discussion Questions:

1. There were four stories shared during the video segment. What are some of the lies the individuals believed about sex?

   This question is intended to elicit personal opinions from the group, as well as lively discussion about the choices that each of the characters in the stories made.

   Some of the lies the individuals believed about sex are:
   -Sex is necessary to keep the relationship alive.
   -If we really love each other, sex is sanctified.
   -Having sex is a rite of passage.

2. Of all the lies described, which one have you come the closest to believing in your life? If you have bought into the lie, how has it impacted your life?

   Building from the previous question, this question is intended to help participants begin to see similarities in their own lives.

3. How would knowing the difference between love and sex have changed the outcomes for:

   Lauren?

   Mike?

   Woman in her 20s?

   Woman in her 30s?

   By answering these questions, participants will be able to envision the dynamics that sex introduces into relationships.

4. How can physical intimacy outside of marriage seem so appealing in one moment and cause such pain later on?

   There are no right or wrong answers here. By raising this question, participants will make note of the lure that often leads to regret. To encourage discussion, ask members to share personal experiences, as well some lies society tells us about physical intimacy outside of marriage.

5. Chip tells us that sex apart from total commitment (marriage) produces manipulation. What does he mean by this?

   Pursuing sex outside of marriage is not an act of love; instead it is a self-serving act that requires manipulation of the other's emotions and desires at the expense of that person's true needs.

ACTION STEPS

This exercise will be a moment of truth for some people. It is very helpful to drive a stake and proclaim your position on an issue. This exercise is an opportunity to do just that. Once you know what you believe, it's much easier to focus on the steps required to back it up.

AT HOME

By taking inventory of the messages around them, the people in your group will be better equipped to recognize wrong thinking as they encounter it in daily life. Moreover, it will then be easier to correct it, or even to eliminate its sources.

SESSION 6

THE DIFFERENCE BETWEEN LOVE AND SEX

Key Point:

In order to fully grasp the seriousness of sexual purity, it's important to understand how our choices about sex impact us at the deepest levels, including the spiritual level. This session addresses head-on some of the reasons why monogamy and abstinence are emphasized by God.

Video Notes

Answer Key:

1. TO uninvolved singles:
   Develop the personal <u>CONVICTION</u> to pursue purity.

2. TO involved singles:
   Develop a <u>STRATEGY</u> to adopt standards of purity.

3. TO people in crisis:
   Get <u>HELP</u>.

4. TO married people:

 TALK about it.

5. TO ALL:

 "Come now, let us REASON together," says the LORD. "Though your sins are like scarlet, they shall be as white as the snow; though they are red as crimson, they shall be like wool." Isaiah 1:18 (NIV)

Notes for Discussion Questions:

1. What does obeying and trusting God in the arena of love and sex look like in your life?

 Ask members to take a snap shot of where they are in this area right now. Then challenge them – are they pleasing God? This question may lead to a separate conversation about where they would like to be in this arena. Encourage such moments of vision-casting, as it will help participants develop a clear picture of what God truly wants for their relationships.

2. How would you define sexual immorality? Why is it impossible to be sexually immoral and grow in your relationship with Christ?

 The purpose of this question is to lead participants to come to some important conclusions about what guidelines for sex are acceptable. At its core, sex that is immoral always hinders our relationship with God because it is idolatry – we take our worship from God and place it on ourselves.

3. Why is sex outside of God's boundaries unloving and destructive in relationships?

 God designed sex to function properly within certain boundaries. When boundaries are observed, those relationships will thrive. When they are violated, relationships are jeopardized. Sex is very powerful. As with anything powerful, it must be handled carefully and obediently.

Leader's Guide
Session Notes

Notes for Discussion Questions: (continued)

4. Why is sexual purity so important to God?
   What steps will you take towards sexual purity in the coming week?

   God created sex as the ultimate expression of human love. It is spiritual communication; therefore it is a high priority to God.

5. Read Isaiah 1:18. What does it say about God's love and plans for us?

   Despite our sin problem (including sexual), God invites us to "reason together" in order to become pure again. This is strong evidence of God's love and mercy.

ACTION STEPS

Whether single, married, or in crisis, there are specific steps of action described in this session. Accordingly, each person in your group should either: develop a personal conviction; develop a strategy; get help; talk about it; or reason together.

AT HOME

Being able to express your personal beliefs about sex is very important. There's no room for wavering on this issue. This exercise is designed to be a moment of truth in which the people in your group can consider God's Word and commit to honor it.

SESSION 7

SEXUAL PURITY IN A SEX-SATURATED WORLD

Key Point:

Sexual purity has a bright side that often gets lost in all the discussion of immorality and its consequences. This session provides important evidence that further suggests that our paradigms for sex and relationships should be shaped by God's design.

Video Notes
Answer Key:

FIVE FACTS ABOUT SEX:

1. Those who abstain from sexual intercourse before marriage report the <u>HIGHEST</u> levels of sexual satisfaction in marriage.

2. Those who cohabitate before marriage have a 50% higher rate of <u>DIVORCE</u> than those who do not.

3. Those who cohabitate are more likely to experience <u>INFIDELITY</u> in marriage.

4. The introduction of sex into a dating relationship almost always ushers in the <u>BREAKUP</u> of the relationship.

5. Sexually-transmitted diseases, including <u>AIDS</u>, can remain <u>DORMANT</u> for up to a decade or more, but can be passed on to others during that time.

HOW TO SAY "YES" TO LOVE AND "NO" TO SECOND-RATE SEX:

I. Loving relationships demand sexual <u>PURITY</u>.

Leader's Guide Session Notes

Notes for Discussion Questions:

1. When you read the 5 facts about sex in the introduction, how outdated does God's wisdom seem concerning sex?

   It's easy to perceive the Bible as ancient and irrelevant; however, when we examine the evidence closely, it consistently offers practical wisdom for living.

2. What are some examples of rules that you're glad exist?

   This question is designed to raise discussion about the benefit of rules. The implication is that rules about sex are for our own good. Ask group members to examine the consequences of not having those rules.

3. Why do you think the idea of delayed gratification motivates some people but not others?

   When it comes right down to it, some people have a problem delaying gratification. This question is designed to foster conversation to help reveal some of the past experiences that have created patterns of instant gratification.

4. Outside of marriage, how far is "too far"? Why?

   *"Too far" is anything intended to gratify one's self, rather than glorify God. As Ephesians 5:9 says, "the fruit of the Light consists in all **goodness** and **righteousness** and **truth**." Our actions are not pleasing to the Lord unless they consist of these things.*

   Everyone should know where he or she stands on this issue. If you haven't decided ahead of time, it will be highly unlikely that your actions will support your ambitions for love and relationships.

5. Which of God's rules about sex feels the most restricting to you? Why?

   Everyone has a particular area of struggle when it comes to purity. This question is intended to generate discussion, and subsequently encouragement, to equip the people in your group to pursue God's standards with success.

ACTION STEPS

The Bible instructs us to have nothing to do with immorality. Furthermore, we are to expose it. Such a stance on sexual impurity would virtually eliminate the possibility of "giving in" in a weak moment. This action step is intended to encourage introspection, prayer, and accountability.

AT HOME

This exercise will help participants declare specific ways they intend to begin experiencing the benefits of sexual purity by taking action this week.

SESSION 8

HOW TO SAY "YES" TO LOVE AND "NO" TO SECOND-RATE SEX

Key Point:

Having laid the theological and philosophical groundwork in previous sessions, this session provides very tactical and strategic steps to implement God's standards for love, sex, and lasting relationships.

Video Notes
Answer Key:

HOW TO SAY "YES" TO LOVE AND "NO" TO SECOND-RATE SEX:

II. Sexual purity demands a GAME PLAN.
   1. Develop CONVICTIONS.
   2. Ponder the CONSEQUENCES.
   3. Make PRE-DECISIONS.
   4. ACCOUNTABILITY.

III. Sexual purity's payoff is awesome!
   1. God's way WORKS!
   2. It's never TOO LATE!
   3. A word to virgins: you are not WEIRD, you are wise!

Leader's Guide
Session Notes

Notes for Discussion Questions:

1. In your own words, what is the difference between "belief" and "conviction"? In what areas of your life do you need to convert your beliefs to convictions?

   As this question suggests, it is crucial to understand the importance of adding intentionality to our beliefs. Unless we have a plan, circumstances will inevitably cause us to compromise what we treasure most.

2. How can fear be a legitimate and healthy motivator for sexual purity?

   There is nothing wrong with fear being a source of motivation. God allows consequences in order to encourage us toward holiness. There are many consequences of sexual impurity that can provide healthy motivation for sexual purity.

3. How does your perception of a person change after learning that he or she is a virgin?

   The culture around us impacts the way we feel about virginity, often depicting it as a drawback. In order to begin valuing virginity, we must first consider our current perception of it.

4. What specific pre-decisions are you going to make to help you win your battle for sexual purity?

   This is a very important question. Participants should name several very specific steps they can take to curb sexual temptation and to ensure sexual purity.

5. Who is the person that can help you develop a game plan and hold you accountable to your commitment to God? What would your game plan need to include?

   This question cannot be overemphasized. Accountability is often the difference between success and failure in the arena of sexual purity. Encourage the people in your group to identify someone with whom they can consult and to whom they will report on the issue of sexual purity in relationships.

ACTION STEPS

This Action Step is a reprise from the Discussion Questions. This will enable participants to consider additional steps in private.

AT HOME

Accountability can be a logistical challenge. Not to mention, it can be intimidating. This assignment is repeated here for additional emphasis on the importance of seeking fellowship and encouragement in this area.

SESSION 9

WAKE UP WORLD! THERE'S A BETTER WAY TO DO RELATIONSHIPS

Key Point:

The most important aspect of pursuing any goal is to have a clear picture of the end result in mind. The goals for this series are fulfilling love, satisfying sex, and relationships that last. In the interest of pursuing those goals, this session focuses on defining a clear picture of the target.

Notes for Discussion Questions:

1. Why is sex such serious business to God? What is at stake for the world around us?

   Sex is an act of spiritual union; therefore it has the power to affect us at the spiritual level. Anything that has spiritual ramifications is serious to God. The spiritual state of the world will determine its overall direction.

Leader's Guide
Session Notes

Notes for Discussion Questions: (continued)

2. Chip described the time he got a vision for the type of family life he wanted. Describe your vision for the family and relationship you've always dreamed of.

   This time of vision-casting is crucial to bringing all the other points of this series down to a focal point.

3. Sexual immorality so violates God's holy character that He tells us not to even speak about it. What does Chip suggest is more powerful than our words?

   Our actions are more powerful than our words.

4. What does Chip mean when he says that your life is a "light"? How can you be an ambassador to pass it on?

   Scripture says that our actions are visible to others and have the power to reveal the sin and darkness in their lives, transmitting God's light in us to them.

5. What would happen if God's church said, "Let's get radical!"? What changes would you need to make in your life to be part of the "Second Sexual Revolution"?

   At its core, this session is about developing vision for the future. This question ties together the concepts of vision and a revolution in sexual purity.

ACTION STEPS

This exercise provides an additional opportunity to examine the role of vision in defining the desired result and providing guidelines for life.

For every prohibitive command, it is important to know the corresponding directive command. In other words, for every "no" there's a corresponding "yes." The "yes" plays a vital role in developing vision and providing motivation to succeed. This exercise will require participants to spend some time in quiet reflection. In addition to recalling specific defining moments and how they responded, this should encourage group members to listen more closely for God's voice in their lives.

SESSION 10

THE SECOND SEXUAL REVOLUTION

Key Point:

To pursue God's standard for sexual purity is to swim against the current of this culture. In fact, it's revolutionary. Anyone who intends to take on such a goal needs to understand the nature of what he or she is attempting. By regarding this venture as a revolution, the person will have the attitude and conviction necessary to succeed.

Video Notes
Answer Key:

ANATOMY OF A SEXUAL REVOLUTION:

I. A revolutionary way to <u>THINK</u> about human sexuality.

II. A revolutionary way to <u>ATTRACT</u> the opposite sex.
   1. Sex is <u>SACRED</u>

   2. Sex is <u>SERIOUS</u>
       1. <u>INWARD</u> Character

       2. <u>OUTWARD</u> Modesty

       3. <u>UPWARD</u> Devotion

Video Notes (continued)

III. A revolutionary way to <u>RELATE</u> to the opposite sex.

    1. As a <u>FRIEND</u>.

    2. As a <u>FAMILY</u> member.

    3. As fellow <u>FOLLOWER</u> <u>OF</u> <u>CHRIST</u>.

Notes for Discussion Questions:

1. Is the time right to start a revolution? Why or why not?
   In your opinion, what does it take to start a revolution?

   The purpose of this question is to prompt further thought about the components of revolutionary thought. In particular, it will cause the people in your group to examine what is necessary to succeed in living sexually-pure lives. They will also be challenged to think about the role they play in changing the world's view of sex.

2. In what ways do you need to change how you think about sex?
   What implications does this have on your thought life? Behavior?
   Viewing habits? Renewing of your mind?

   This is the final session, and hopefully your group has reached a deeper level of intimacy with one another. Encourage group members to be open and honest in their discussion as they name specific action steps for pursuing sexual purity.

3. How does modesty facilitate loving and lasting relationships?
   In what ways has our culture seduced us into attracting the opposite sex in ways that focus on outer versus inner qualities?

   As this question suggests, sexual impurity is often fueled by immodesty. Hollywood and the media continually push the boundaries of modesty — what is scandalous today will be stylish tomorrow. Emphasizing modesty helps us focus on the root cause of much impurity.

4. Is it possible that the whole "dating paradigm" is not the wisest or most effective way to build relationships with the opposite sex? Explain.

The dating paradigm can be damaging when it automatically leads to greater and greater sexual temptation. Society's model suggests a natural progression from one physical and emotional stage to the next. By the world's standards, there are built-in expectations that make it normal to give in to sexual temptation.

5. How could you answer God's call to the "Second Sexual Revolution"? What might that look like in your life and relationships?

This question is a final vision-casting exercise, inviting participants to describe their steps toward a revolution in sexual purity.

ACTION STEPS

This exercise will enable the people in your group to give additional consideration to the points from the video part of the session. Participants can apply the message by clarifying the perspective they need to embrace regarding the opposite sex.

AT HOME

This exercise is designed to put what you've learned into practice. For the revolution to be successful, we must first change how we think and go about doing relationships. That means we must be intentional about the changes God's calling us to make in our lives. Encourage your group to answer the question, then turn the page and make a personal covenant with God to become a part of the second sexual revolution!

Love, Sex & Lasting Relationships

Love, Sex & Lasting Relationships

Love, Sex & Lasting Relationships